MAKING THE GRADE · G

EASY POPULAR PIECES FOR YOUNG VIOLINISTS. SELECTED AND ARR/

3

Chester Music
part of The Music Sales Group
London/New York/Paris/Sydney/Copenhagen/Berlin/Madrid/Tokyo/Hong Kong

Published by
Chester Music
14-15 Berners Street, London, W1T 3LJ, England.

Exclusive Distributors:
Music Sales Limited
Distribution Centre, Newmarket Road, Bury St. Edmunds, Suffolk IP33 3YB, England.
Music Sales Pty Limited
20 Resolution Drive, Caringbah, NSW 2229, Australia.

Order No. CH78573

Music arranged and processed by Jerry Lanning.
Edited by Heather Ramage.
Printed in the EU.

www.musicsales.com

INTRODUCTION

This collection of 51 popular tunes has been carefully arranged and graded to provide attractive teaching repertoire for young violinists. The familiarity of the material will stimulate pupils' enthusiasm and encourage their practice.

The technical demands of the solo part increase progressively up to the standard of Associated Board Grade 3. The piano accompaniments are simple yet effective and should be within the range of most pianists.

Practical suggestions for bowing are given, but these may of course be adapted to suit the needs of the individual student. It is important always to feel a steady pulse, so that bow speeds can be planned appropriately.

MAKING THE GRADE · GRADES 1-3

GRADE 1

GRADE 2

GRADE 3

ANY DREAM WILL DO

(from "Joseph and the Amazing Technicolor® Dreamcoat")

Music by Andrew Lloyd Webber. Lyrics by Tim Rice

Take care with the dotted rhythms. Keep the semiquavers light and try to match the accompaniment.

THE SKATER'S WALTZ

By Emil Waldteufel

Make your bow changes as smooth as possible.

EENSY, WEENSY SPIDER

American traditional

The tempo should be quick enough to feel two beats in a bar.

PAVANE

(from "The Capriol Suite")

By Peter Warlock

Try for a smooth, sustained sound, and be aware of the four bar phrases.

I'M POPEYE THE SAILOR MAN

Words & Music by Sammy Lerner

This piece needs a bright and breezy performance!

EDELWEISS

(from "The Sound of Music")

Words by Oscar Hammerstein II. Music by Richard Rodgers

Play each phrase as smoothly as possible. Listen carefully to the tuning.

18
mf
mf

24
mp
mp

29

O NO, JOHN!

English traditional

Play the last four bars quite forcefully, for contrast.

SARABANDE

(from "Keyboard Suite IX")

By George Frideric Handel

Pay careful attention to the rests in this piece.

I HAVE A DREAM

Words & Music by Benny Andersson & Björn Ulvaeus

Be sure to hold the long notes for their full length.

15
20
25
30

THE YELLOW ROSE OF TEXAS

American traditional

Play with a full sound, and try not to drag.

JEAN DE FLORETTE (THEME)

By Jean-Claude Petit

Although this is a gentle piece, use enough bow to develop a good sound.

NO MATTER WHAT

Music by Andrew Lloyd Webber. Words by Jim Steinman

Take care with the start of each phrase. It's very easy to be late!

13
17
21
24
poco rit.

HEY HEY ARE YOU READY TO PLAY

(Tweenies Theme)

Music by Graham Pike & Liz Kitchen. Words by Will Brenton & Ian Lauchlan

Listen hard to the tuning of the octave leaps. Keep the rhythm relaxed.

10
13
16
19

GUANTANAMERA

Music adaption by Pete Seeger & Julian Orbon. Words adapted by Julian Orbon from a poem by José Marti

Keep the rhythm very steady. When a phrase ends with a quaver, play the quaver lightly.

16
20
24
27

BARBIE GIRL

Words & Music by Soren Rasted, Claus Norreen, Rene Dif,
Lene Nystrom, Johnny Pederson & Karsten Delgado

Take care not to hold on to the quaver at the end of bar four.

THE PHANTOM OF THE OPERA

(from "The Phantom of the Opera")

Music by Andrew Lloyd Webber. Lyrics by Charles Hart. Additional lyrics by Richard Stilgoe and Mike Batt.

Be absolutely precise with the dotted crotchet/quaver rhythms.

LAND OF HOPE AND GLORY

By Edward Elgar

Try for a very smooth, sustained sound. Don't let the tempo drag.

19
25
cresc.
cresc.
31
mf
mf
37
dim.
dim.

ALL MY LOVING

Words & Music by John Lennon and Paul McCartney

Be careful to read the rhythms carefully – don't guess!

16
1.
2.
21
26
31

SOMETHIN' STUPID

Words & Music by C. Carson Parks

Articulate the repeated quavers neatly and evenly.

10
13
16
19

OOM PAH PAH

(from "Oliver")

Words & Music by Lionel Bart

This piece needs a strong performance, but the middle section should be softer and smoother for contrast.

26
32
f
f
39
46

DANCE TO YOUR DADDY

English traditional

Accent the first beat of each bar slightly, but play the other notes quite lightly.

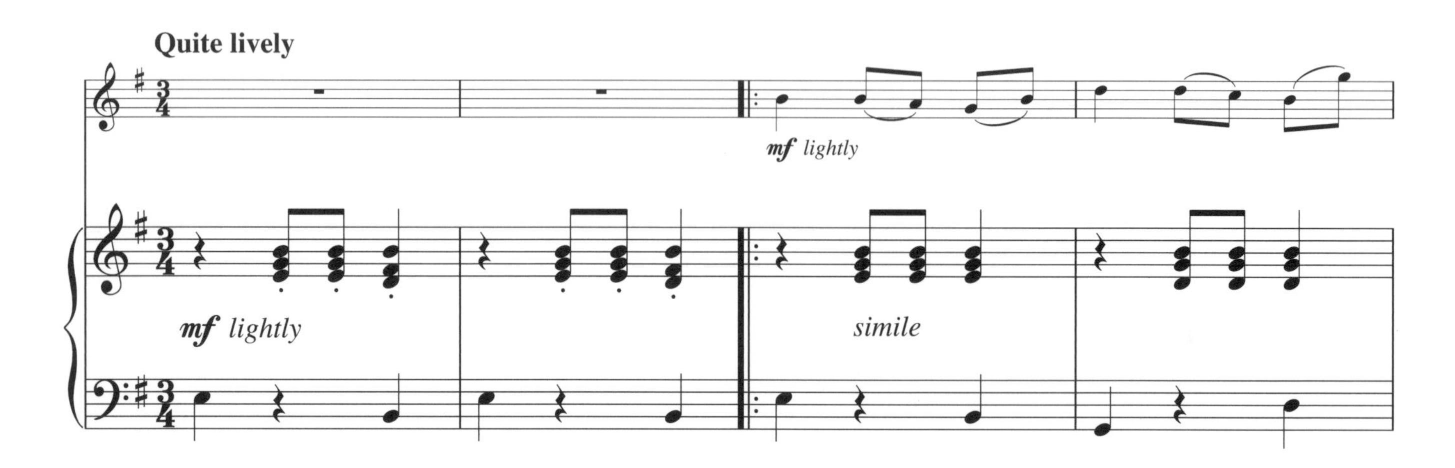

GREENSLEEVES

Traditional.

This tune dates from Elizabethan times.
Notice that the Gs are sometimes sharp and sometimes natural.

ANNIE'S SONG

Words & Music by John Denver.

'Annie's Song' was made popular as a flute solo by James Galway.
Play it as smoothly as possible, and make sure you hold all the notes for their full value.
Start in the middle of the bow.

20
25
30
1.
35
2.
rit.
p
rit.
p

SAILING

Words & Music by Gavin Sutherland.

This was a big hit for Rod Stewart.
Don't forget to slow down the bow for the minims.

9
1.
mf
mf
11
2.
14
17
rit.
rit.

IMAGINE

Words & Music by John Lennon.

Start in the upper half of the bow.
Notice the way the opening two-bar phrase is repeated, with slight variations.
If you have problems with bar 15, practise it slowly, counting in quavers.

13
cresc.
mf
cresc.
mf
16
mp
mp
19
22
rit.
4
3
rit.

MULL OF KINTYRE

Words & Music by McCartney & Laine

Look out for the quaver/dotted crotchet group in bar 4 and elsewhere, and make sure the rhythm is really accurate. Push through the whole bow on the last crotchet so that you have enough bow to sustain the final G.

f
f
dim. e rit.
dim. e rit.

SKYE BOAT SONG

Traditional.

This is one of the best known Scottish melodies. It needs a sustained sound and smooth playing.

13
17
p
p
21
25

NELLIE THE ELEPHANT

Words by Ralph Butler. Music by Peter Hart.

Watch out for the key change.
This piece starts in G minor, but the chorus is in G major.

Moderately

mp

mp

5

8

1.

2. *ten.*

ten.

12
mf
mf
16
20
24

TULIPS FROM AMSTERDAM

English Words by Gene Martyn. Original Words by Neumann & Bader. Music by Ralf Arnie.

Here's a cheerful tune. It's not very difficult, but needs to swing along at a good pace. Notice the D sharps towards the end.

22
27
cresc. poco a poco
cresc. poco a poco
33
f
f
39

AUTUMN FROM 'THE FOUR SEASONS'

By Antonio Vivaldi.

This theme comes from one of the most popular works in the classical repertoire. The quavers need lots of energy and should not be too *legato*. The opening phrase is repeated *piano*, an octave lower.

THE GIFT TO BE SIMPLE

Traditional Shaker Hymn.

Also known as 'The Lord Of The Dance', this very well known hymn tune was used by the American composer Aaron Copland in his ballet 'Appalachian Spring'.

Keep your bow moving through the slurs.

CASTLE ON A CLOUD

Music by Claude-Michel Schönberg. Lyrics by Herbert Kretzmer.
Original text by Alain Boublil & Jean-Marc Natel.

If you can, try the opening phrase in third position for a mellow sound.

12
14
p
p
17
20
poco rit.
poco rit.

WHO DO YOU THINK YOU ARE KIDDING MR HITLER?

Words by Jimmy Perry. Music by Jimmy Perry and Derek Taverner.

You will recognise this as the theme from the very popular TV series 'Dad's Army'.
Look out for the accidentals, and pay special attention to the final phrase.

March tempo

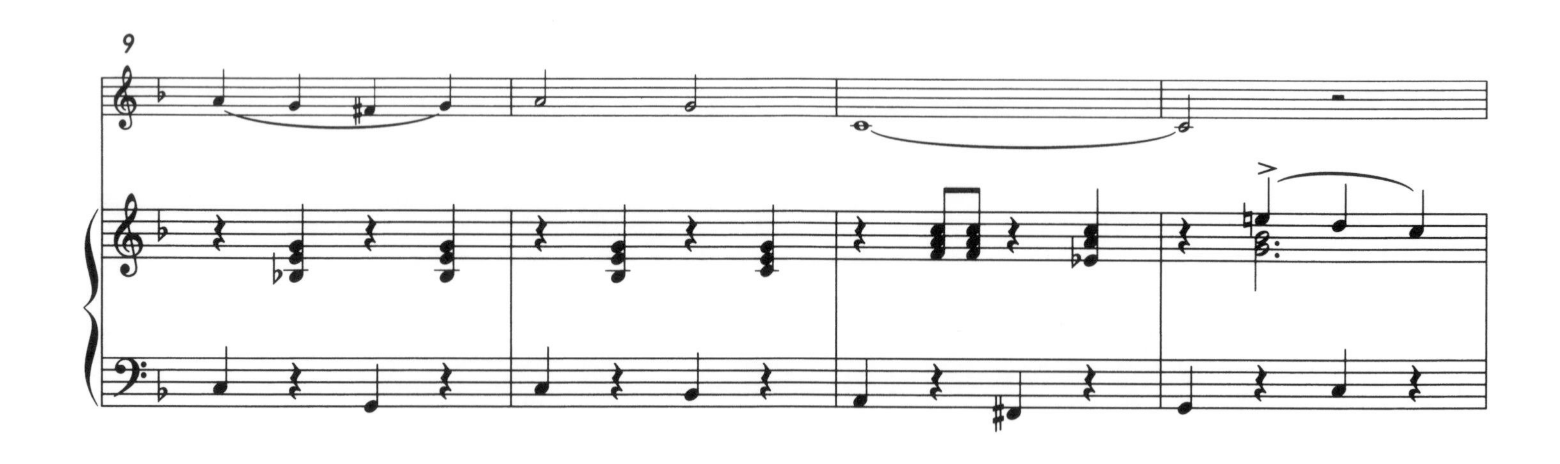

13
17
21
25
f
f
sfz

LEAVING ON A JET PLANE

Words & Music by John Denver.

In bar 5 and similar places don't be late playing the second quaver, and accent it slightly.

16
20
24
28
1.
2.
rall.
rall.

VINCENT

Words & Music by Don McLean.

Keep a steady tempo, and let the quaver passages flow smoothly.
At bar 17 you may find third position easier.

14
17
mf
mf
21
25
rall.
p
rall.
p

ASLAN'S THEME FROM 'THE CHRONICLES OF NARNIA'

By Geoffrey Burgon.

Try for a different sound in the minor section to contrast with a warm opening.

13

D.C. al ⊕ Coda
16

⊕ Coda
19
f
f

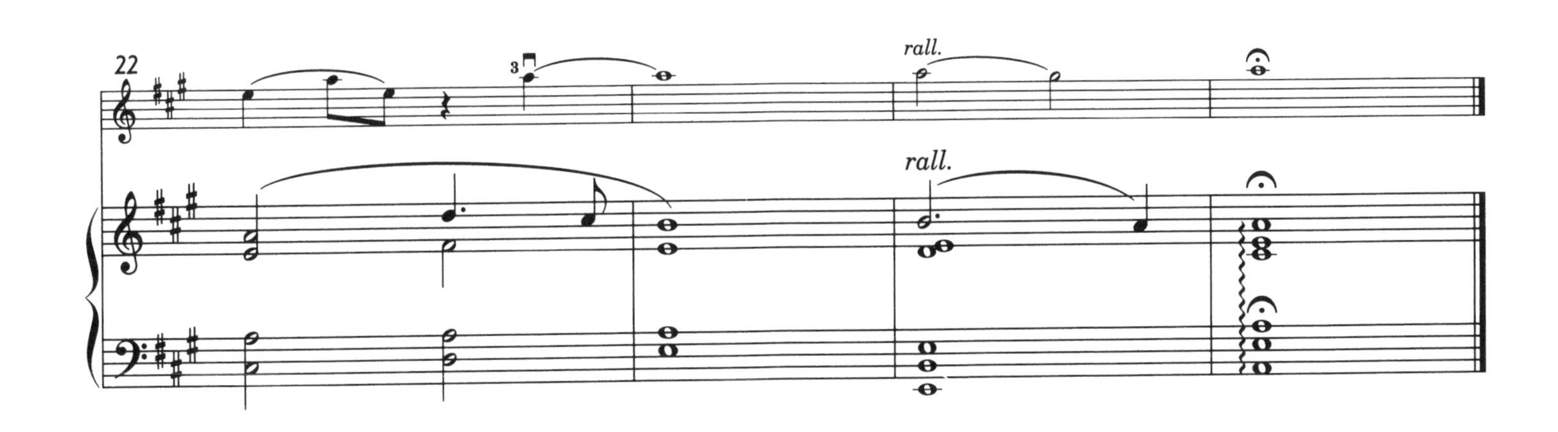
22
rall.
rall.

HAVAH NAGILAH

Traditional.

'Havah Nagilah' is a well-known traditional Jewish song.
Notice that D sharp is often followed by C natural (not C sharp).
Practise your E harmonic minor scale before tackling this piece.

17
1.
2.
mf
mf
21
Moderately
gradually faster
cresc.
cresc.
25
f
f
29

32
35
mf
mf
39
4
43
1.
2.
3
3
f
f

THE INCREDIBLE HULK (THEME FROM)

Composed by Joe Harnell.

This theme from the TV series is a wistful and attractive melody, which reflects the gentle side of the Hulk's nature, so bow very lightly through the slurs.

13
mf
16
1.
19
p
mp
22
2.

25
f
mf
2
f
mf
28
31
p
p
34

YESTERDAY

Words & Music by John Lennon & Paul McCartney.

Most peoples' favourite Beatles song. Notice the F sharp and G sharp in the ascending scale of A melodic minor (bar 4), followed by the F and G naturals in the descending scale. The fingering relates to first and third positions, but if you feel daring try the whole piece in the second position.

A little slower

SUMMERTIME

By George Gershwin, Ira Gershwin, DuBose & Dorothy Heyward.

'Summertime' is probably Gershwin's most famous tune. The notes aren't difficult, but be careful that you play the correct rhythm in bars 11 and 12. Play the long notes with vibrato if possible.

13
3
16
1.
19
mp
22
2.
3
p
dim.
dim.

EL CONDOR PASA (IF I COULD)

Musical Arrangement by J. Milchberg & D. Robles. English Lyric by Paul Simon.

This is a traditional melody from South America, made popular by Simon and Garfunkel.

Keep a very steady tempo.

13
mf
16
19
22
dim. e rall.
p
dim. e rall.
p

YELLOW SUBMARINE

Words & Music by John Lennon & Paul McCartney.

This Beatles number needs to be played with a tight, accurate rhythm — don't slip into triplets in the chorus, and don't use too much bow. Notice that the verse is repeated an octave higher.

16
19
f
f
22
25
1.
2. poco rit.
poco rit.

BRIDGE OVER TROUBLED WATER

Words & Music by Paul Simon.

Here is Paul Simon's most enduring song.

Try for a full, rounded tone as the piece builds to a climax around bar 23.

15
mf
3
mf
3
2
19
23
f
f
mf
mf
27
rit.
rit.

ITSY BITSY, TEENIE WEENIE, YELLOW POLKADOT BIKINI

Words & Music by Lee Pockriss & Paul J. Vance.

If you want to leave out the spoken sections, you can cut from the first beat of bar 10 to the second beat of bar 12, and cut bar 22 completely. Watch out for the $\frac{2}{4}$ bar.

13
16
19
1.
Two, three, four,
22
2.
Stick a - round we'll tell you more.

JEANIE WITH THE LIGHT BROWN HAIR

Words & Music by Stephen Foster.

This song needs really expressive playing.
Be particularly careful of the slurred ninth (A to B) in bar 14. The B should be really soft.
Don't grip the neck too tightly when you change position.

10

13
mf
dim.
p
mf
dim.
p

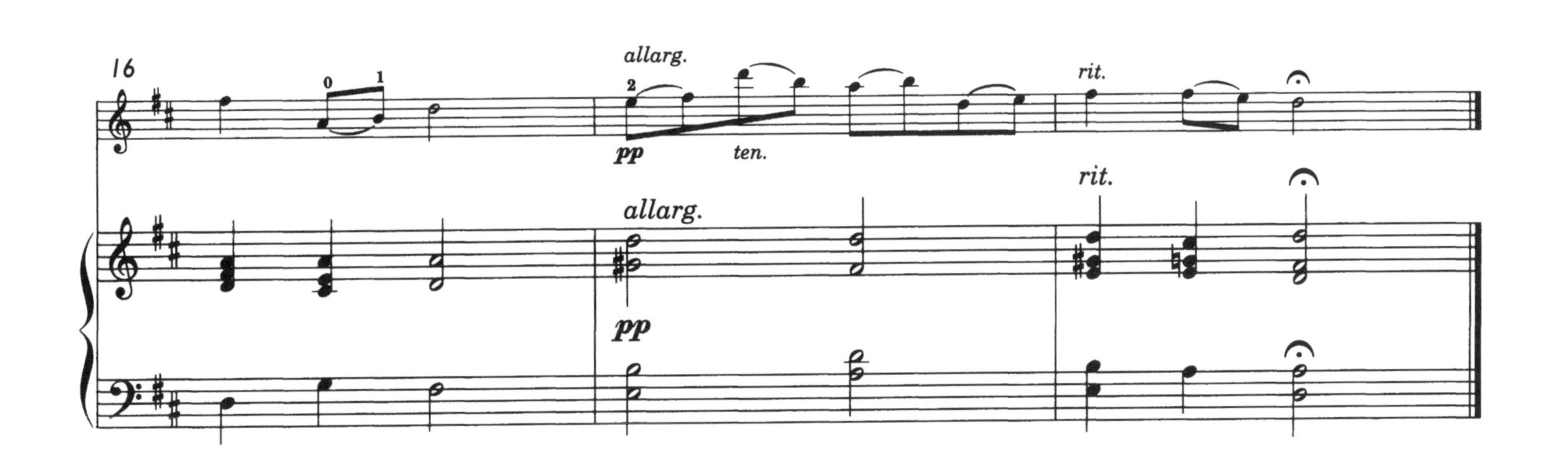
16
allarg.
rit.
pp
ten.
rit.
allarg.
pp

I KNOW HIM SO WELL

Words & Music by Benny Andersson, Tim Rice & Bjorn Ulvaeus.

Many of the notes are slurred in pairs,
which should be practised carefully to ensure that the bow is shared equally between both quavers.

10
1.
2.
mf
mf
13
16
19
rall.
rall.

ONE MOMENT IN TIME

Words & Music by Albert Hammond & John Bettis.

Make sure your bow speed is appropriate for the varying durations of each bow.

17
20
24
28
rall.
rall.

BIRDIE SONG / BIRDIE DANCE

Words & Music by Werner Thomas & Terry Rendall.

Articulate the quavers in the first section clearly, playing off the string if you can. If not, grip the string with little bows for a similar effect.

14
simile
18
22
26

HE AIN'T HEAVY HE'S MY BROTHER

Words by Bob Russell. Music by Bobby Scott.

Some of the rhythms are a bit tricky in this piece. If you have trouble with them, practise each phrase slightly slower, counting in quavers. Be careful to count the rests in bar 21.

13
3

17
1.

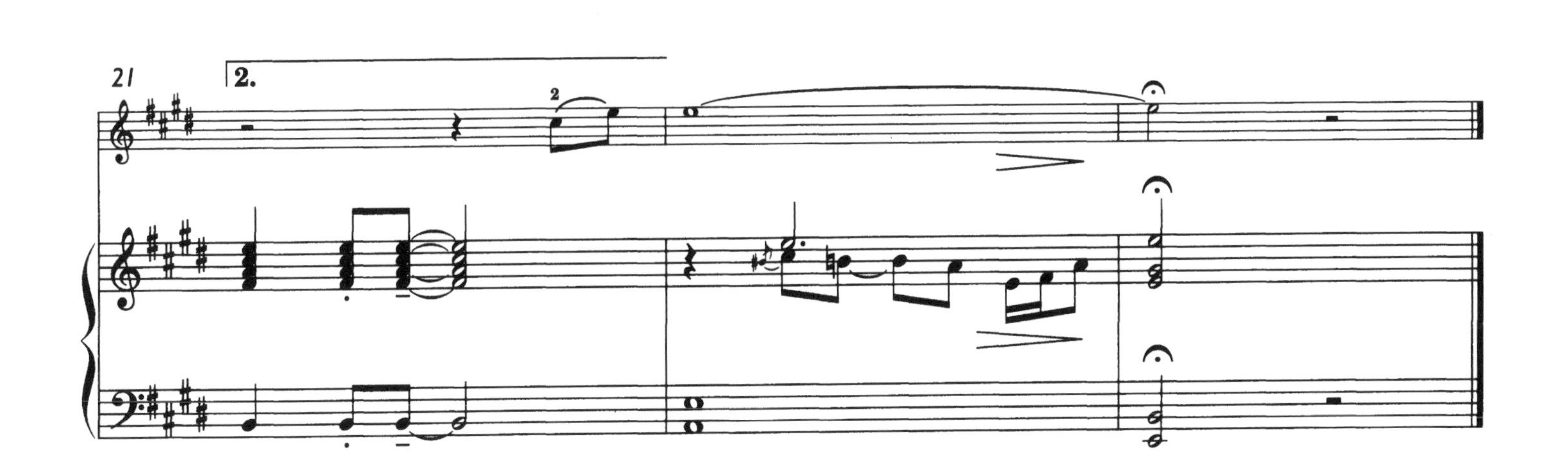
21
2.

AMERICA

Music by Leonard Bernstein. Lyrics by Stephen Sondheim

In this lively number from 'West Side Story' the time signature alternates between $\frac{6}{8}$ and $\frac{3}{4}$;
you will need to keep this clearly in mind in bars 17 to 25.
In the latter section push the up bows before the accented notes.

18
23
mf
ff
27
f
f
31
1.
2.

THE ENTERTAINER

By Scott Joplin.

This piano rag featured in the film 'The Sting'. Make sure you keep a very steady tempo.
You will find that the piece is quite a test of stamina.

13
mp
mp
f
f
16
To Coda
1.
2.
19
mf
mf
23

27
4
4
30
33
p
p
37
1.
2.
D.𝄋 al ⊕ Coda
1
2
mp
⊕ Coda